Contents

Answers to the questions are on the back of the Pull-out Poster in the centre of the book.

This book covers unit 6E from the year six scheme of work

Published by Coordination Group Publications Ltd.

Contributors:
Angela Billington
Chris Dennett
Lindsay Jordan
Tim Major
Katherine Stewart
Claire Thompson
Tim Wakeling
James Paul Wallis
Suzanne Worthington

ISBN: 978 1 84146 273 8

Groovy website: www.cgpbooks.co.uk

Jolly bits of clipart from CorelDRAW®

Printed by Elanders Hindson Ltd, Newcastle upon Tyne.

Text, design, layout and original illustrations © Coordination Group Publications Ltd. 2000

Background

When you <u>push</u> or <u>pull</u> something, that's a force.

Q1 Here's a tiny horse dragging a weight with a forcemeter. Look at both pictures and answer the questions about the forcemeter.

FORCEMETER

a) What does it measure?

....

Kitchen tiles   Grass

b) What makes the pointer move? ....

c) If the horse is pulling at the same speed each time, which surface will give a bigger reading — the kitchen tiles or the grass? ....

Q2 Write next to each pair of magnets what they'll do to each other — 'attract' or 'repel'.

....

Q3 Here's a horseshoe hanging on an elastic band. What will happen to the band if...

a) I swap the horseshoe for a heavier one?

....

b) I hang a lighter horseshoe on it? ....

Q4 a) What makes these parachutes fall slowly?

....

....

b) Tick ✔ the one that will fall more slowly.

Q5 In each of these pictures, (circle) the arrow that shows the right direction of the force named under the picture.

Rabbit's pull on carrot   Man's push on trolley

A horse pulling a forcemeter — a horsemeter?...

The thing with names of things in science is that they seem so <u>complicated</u> and <u>weird</u>, but they're really just <u>common sense</u>. Like forcemeters — they measure forces. No great surprise there.

Gravity

Gravity holds us, and everything else, down on the <u>ground</u> where we should be.
It's great — if it wasn't for gravity we'd all be <u>floating around</u> and bumping our heads
on the ceiling. But gravity has its bad side too — like when you fall out of a tree.

Q1   Read the weights showing on the forcemeters for the four different
objects. Write the 'objects' and their weights in the table below.
Read the scales carefully — not all the forcemeters are the same.

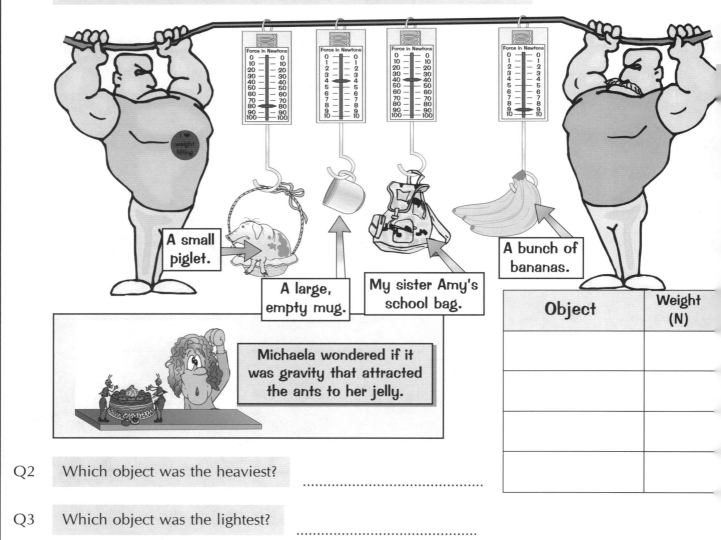

Object	Weight (N)

Q2   Which object was the heaviest?   ....

Q3   Which object was the lightest?   ....

Q4   Circle the right words in this sentence so that it makes sense as a conclusion.

What we call the SIZE / WEIGHT of an object is the force that attracts it

TOWARDS / AWAY FROM the Earth. The HEAVIER / LIGHTER something is,

the bigger the RUBBER BAND / FORCE that pulls it towards the Earth.

Gravity — a very down to earth subject...

You measure weight in <u>Newtons</u> — weight is how strongly the Earth's gravity pulls something.
<u>Gravity</u> is a force that pulls things towards the Earth — it's what keeps you on the ground.

Gravity

Gravity on the Earth is the most <u>important</u> kind of gravity for you and me — you need it every day. But you don't only get gravity on the Earth — it exists on the <u>Moon</u> as well. But it's not as strong as on the Earth — the Earth's gravity is six times stronger than the Moon's.

Earth

Buoyant Barry the astronaut and his spacedog Bouncing Bozo both love jumping.

They had a go at jumping on the Earth and jumping on the Moon.

On the Earth gravity is about six times stronger than it is on the Moon — this meant they could jump loads higher on the Moon.

Moon

Q1 Answer these questions — remember gravity is six times stronger on the Earth than it is on the Moon.

Tanya and her apple weigh 12 Newtons on Earth. About how much would they weigh on the Moon? Circle the right answer.

a) 12 ÷ 2 = 6N   b) 12 ÷ 6 = 2N   c) 12 ÷ 12 = 1N

I hung my fish from a rubber band, and measured how much the rubber band stretched. If the rubber band stretched 6 cm on the Earth, how much would it have stretched on the Moon? (Clue: it will be six times more on the Earth.)

....

Whacking Wilma, the top class golfer, can hit a golf ball 400 metres on the Earth. Would she be able to hit it further, or not as far, on the Moon?

....

Q2 Walking on the Moon is a tad different because gravity isn't as strong and doesn't hold you down as well. Write a description of how you think it would feel to walk on the Moon.

....

....

....

What on Earth's getting you down? — gravity...

Gravity pulls everything towards everything else. With ordinary things like two apples, the pull is so weak you'd <u>never notice it</u>. You need <u>huge</u> things like planets to be able to feel it.

Gravity

The Earth is a great big <u>sphere</u> and gravity pulls you towards its centre. So gravity isn't really pulling you downwards — it's pulling you towards the <u>centre</u> of the Earth.
OK, maybe it's a bit confusing, but this page should make it all a lot clearer.

When Cedric isn't playing with his yo-yo it hangs straight down.
He uses it to measure whether things are <u>upright</u> or not.
The name for a piece of string with a weight on the end is a <u>plumb line</u>.

Q1   Explain why Cedric's yo-yo hangs straight down.

....

....

Q2   Two of Cedric's cousins have gone on holiday. Cedric and his cousins are all holding their yo-yos to make plumb lines. Two of them have been drawn onto this picture already — draw the third one and his plumb line where the number 3 is.

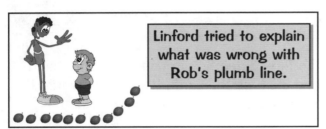

Linford tried to explain what was wrong with Rob's plumb line.

Q3   Look at this picture of the Earth surrounded by rain clouds.
a) When the rain falls, which way will it fall (if there's no wind)?

....

....

b) Draw some rain onto the picture.

Q4   My friends Laura, Ed and Malcolm in Australia don't have any trouble standing up and walking around. Why don't they fall off the Earth?

....

....

Where do plumbers queue? — In a plumb line...

Gravity pulls you towards the <u>centre of the Earth</u>, not just 'downwards'. People on other parts of the world get pulled towards the centre, too — not towards what we think of as 'down'.

Multiple Forces

You can have more than one force on an object at once. Even if something is lying <u>dead still</u> on a table, it still has the force of <u>gravity</u> pulling it towards the Earth. What stops it crashing through the floor into the centre of the planet is an <u>upward force</u> from the table.

Q1 Each of these pictures shows two forces acting in opposite directions. In each example, label the two arrows to show what the forces are.

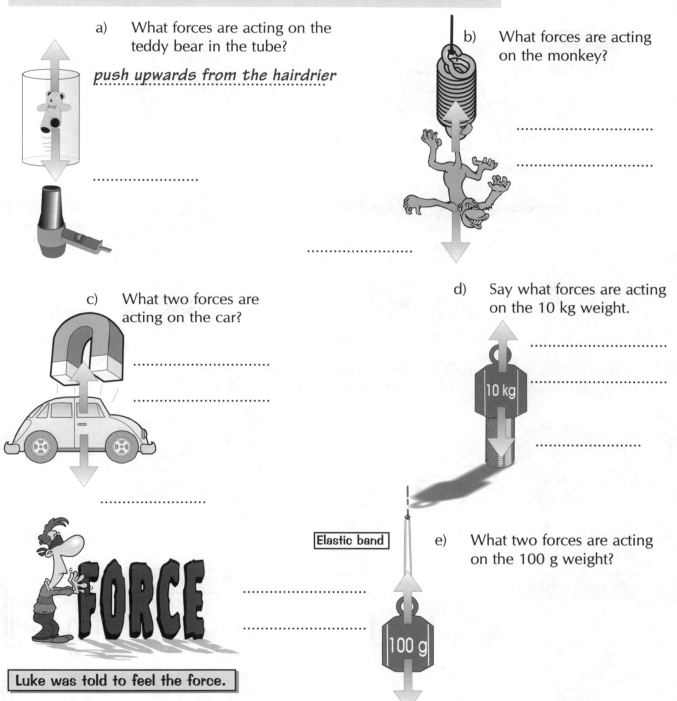

a) What forces are acting on the teddy bear in the tube?

push upwards from the hairdrier
....

b) What forces are acting on the monkey?
....
....
....

c) What two forces are acting on the car?
....
....
....

d) Say what forces are acting on the 10 kg weight.
....
....
....

Luke was told to feel the force.

Elastic band
....
....

e) What two forces are acting on the 100 g weight?
....

If this isn't much fun — force yourself to do it...

Thank goodness everything is <u>balanced</u> with two forces — if there was <u>only gravity</u> you'd fall through the floor. And if there was <u>only</u> a force upwards you'd fly off into space. Not what you want.

Multiple Forces

Pairs of forces don't <u>have</u> to include gravity — they could be made up of any other two forces.
Like when you arm-wrestle someone — that's two forces in <u>opposite</u> directions.

Q1   In each of these pictures there are two forces labelled. Draw an
arrow for each force, to show what direction the force is acting in.

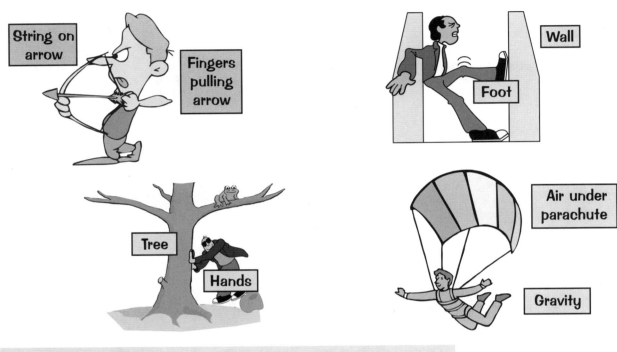

Q2   Some of the arrows are pointing the wrong way in two of these
pictures. Put a tick ✔ in the box if the forces are shown correctly.

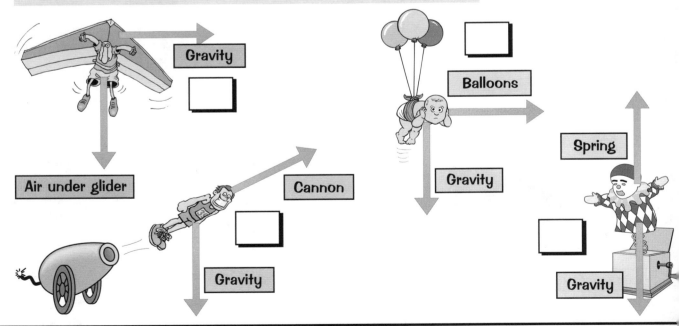

Octopus in a gym — multi-pull forces...

If there's a force in one direction, there's often one in the <u>other</u> direction that's <u>resisting</u> it.
If the forces are the <u>same strength</u>, they cancel each other out — that's called <u>balancing forces</u>.

<u>Multiple Forces</u>

What you've got to remember is that gravity always pulls things <u>towards the centre of the Earth</u>. Anything which is pushing away from the Earth, or stopping something from falling, is <u>working against</u> gravity.

Q1 I'm not giving you any help here. This time you've got to say where the forces are coming from <u>and</u> draw the arrows to show the direction they're acting in.

Andrea found a new way to slow the effect of gravity.

<u>Stuff gravity — I'm working against it...</u>

Gravity always pulls <u>towards</u> the centre of the Earth, so whenever you have to do one of these questions, you know the gravity arrow points <u>downwards</u>. For the other forces you have to <u>think</u>.

Forces in Water

When you hold something underwater, it doesn't feel as heavy as when it's in air.
I decided to do an investigation on how much things weigh in air and in water,
by hanging some things from forcemeters.

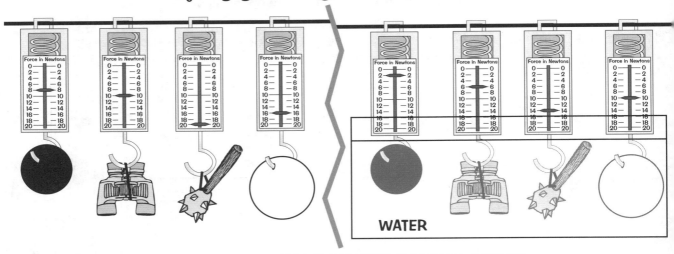

WATER

Q1 Look at the forcemeters in the picture, and fill in this table of the weights of the objects in air and in water. I've done the first one for you.

	Black Ball	Binoculars	Spiky Club	White Ball
Weight in air (in Newtons)	8			
Weight in water (in Newtons)	2			

Just when you thought it was safe to go in the water...

Miss Jones loved scaring the headmaster.

Q2 Look at the results in the table. Which of these is the right <u>description</u> of the results? Choose the right one, and write it out on the dots below.

The objects were heavier in the water.

The objects didn't weigh anything in the water.

The objects weighed less in water than they did in air.

The forcemeters weighed more in the air than in the water.

....

Q3 Choose from the words on the fish to finish this <u>explanation</u> of <u>why</u> your answer to Q2 is what happens.

When an object is under the .... , the water gives

it an .... push that ....

some of the object's ....

weight   upward   downward   cancels out   adds to   water

Forces in water — that'll be the Navy...

Water cancels out some of the gravity because it's <u>pushing upwards</u>. That makes things weigh less in water. That's why you can <u>float</u> on water if you hold your breath — not like on air...

Forces in Water

I've found out that water pushes upwards and changes the weight of things. But now I want to know if the <u>size</u> of the object makes a difference to the upwards push of water.

I did an experiment using four hollow balls made of modelling clay.

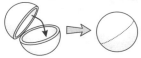

Each ball weighed 300 g.

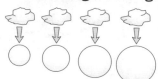

I hung each ball from a forcemeter, first in air, then in water.

When the balls were in the water, the water gave them an upward push.

Q1 You can work out the amount of upward push by working out the difference between the forcemeter reading in air and in water. Fill these values in the last column of the table. I've done the first one for you.

For adding and subtracting decimals, see page 20 of the Key Stage 2 Maths Study Book.

Size of Hollow Ball	Forcemeter Reading in Air (Newtons)	Forcemeter Reading in Water (Newtons)	Upward Push from the Water (Newtons)
Small ◯	3.0	2.5	_0·5_
Medium ◯	3.0	2.0	
Large ◯	3.0	1.5	
Extra Large ◯	3.0	1.0	

Q2 Complete this bar chart to show the amount of upward push given to the different-sized balls.

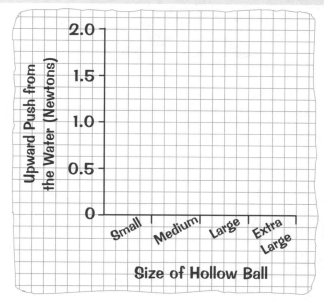

I know this page is about water giving an upwards push, but this is ridiculous...

Q3 (Circle) the right words in the brackets to finish this conclusion about the experiment.

[GRAVY / GRAVITY] pulls things towards the ground and gives them weight. The water gives things an

[UPWARD / DOWNWARD] push that [ADDS TO / BALANCES OUT] some of the weight. The bigger

an object is, the [SMALLER / BIGGER] the [UPWARD / DOWNWARD] push from the water is.

<u>Why is water fit? — it does loads of push-ups...</u>

The <u>bigger</u> the object, the <u>stronger</u> the upward push of the water. That's why great big, hulking blue whales can float around gracefully in water — but they can't move at all on land.

Forces in Water

Gravity <u>pulls</u> things down towards the Earth. But things in water get an upward push — even if they're only partly in the water.

Q1   Draw a stripy arrow ⬇ on all the things in the picture being pulled down by gravity. Draw a spotty arrow ⬆ on all the things getting an upward push from the <u>water</u>. I've done one for you.

Doctor, doctor, I think I'm a limpet — get a grip...

Gravity pulls one way and the water pushes the other — but it <u>doesn't</u> feel the same as having two mates pulling your arms in opposite directions. It feels like you weigh less — neat really.

Doing Things More Than Once

Ogbert and Ugmina both did an experiment about how much things weigh in water and in air.

They made four hollow balls out of modelling clay.

Each ball weighed 500 g.

They hung each ball from a forcemeter, first in air, then in water. When the balls were in the water, the water gave them an upward push.

Here are their results:

Ogbert's Results

Size of Hollow Ball	Small ◯	Medium ◯	Large ◯	Extra Large ◯
Forcemeter Reading in Air (Newtons)	5.0	5.0	5.0	5.0
Forcemeter Reading in Water (Newtons)	4.0	3.2	1.8	1.2
Upward Push from the Water (Newtons)	1.0	1.8	3.2	3.8

Ugmina's Results

Size of Hollow Ball	Small ◯	Medium ◯	Large ◯	Extra Large ◯
Forcemeter Reading in Air (Newtons)	5.0	5.0	5.0	5.0
Forcemeter Reading in Water (Newtons)	3.6	3.0	1.4	0.8
Upward Push from the Water (Newtons)	1.4	2.0	3.6	4.2

Q1 Draw a bar chart of the upward push from the water. Draw red bars for Ogbert's results, and yellow bars for Ugmina's results.

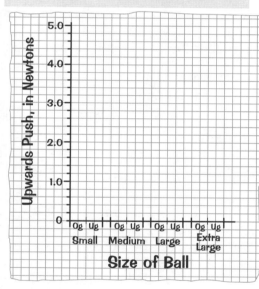

They both used the same balls and the same forcemeter.

Q2 a) Did they always get the same results?

....

b) If you answered 'no', describe any pattern you can see in the difference between their results. (For example, did Ogbert always get higher results than Ugmina?)

....

....

....

....

....

NO!

Iggy kept trying to eat the apparatus.

Q3 Why might they have got different results? Circle the right words in the brackets.

Sometimes it's [EASY / DIFFICULT] to read the forcemeter accurately,

because the [POINTER / FLOOR] can wobble up and down a bit.

Q4 The closer their results were, the more sure you can be that the results are right. For which of the balls would you be most sure about the result? Tick ✔ the right box.

Small ☐   Large ☐

Medium ☐   Extra Large ☐

Doing things more than once, more than once, more than once...

When you do an experiment, make sure your <u>readings</u> are really <u>accurate</u>. Not everyone will get <u>exactly</u> the same results, but they should be roughly the same. The experiment's no earthly use otherwise.

Doing Things More Than Once

Bob, Liz, Ed, Sue and Nav all did an experiment.
They all used the same equipment, but they **didn't** all get exactly the same results.

The experiment is to drop different-sized balls through a water-filled cylinder. They use a stopwatch to time how long it takes them to go from the 'start' line to the 'stop' line.

The balls were hollow, and all weighed the **same**.

Q1 Finish off this table of the results. Use the notepad to fill in the table with Nav's results.

Size of Hollow Ball	Small ◯	Medium ◯	Large ◯	Extra Large ◯
Bob's Results	0.9 secs	1.4 secs	1.7 secs	2.0 secs
Liz's Results	1.2 secs	1.5 secs	1.7 secs	2.0 secs
Ed's Results	1.2 secs	1.4 secs	1.6 secs	2.0 secs
Sue's Results	1.1 secs	1.3 secs	1.5 secs	1.9 secs
Nav's Results				

Nav's Results

The small ball took 1.1 seconds.

The medium ball took 1.5 seconds.

The large ball took 1.7 seconds.

The extra large ball took 2.0 seconds.

Q2 Tick ✔ the right box to show which of these is the **best** description of all the results at once.

[ ] The small ball fell quickly.

[ ] A medium-sized ball falls in about one and a half seconds.

[ ] The smaller the ball is, the slower it falls.

[ ] The bigger the ball is, the slower it falls.

Q3 Finish this explanation of the results. Write 'same', 'more', 'less', 'bigger' or 'smaller' in each blank.

The .... the ball, the more it's slowed down by the water resistance and the air trapped inside. All the balls weighed the .... , so they were all pulled down by gravity the .... But the bigger the ball, the .... the upward push it gets from the water, so it's pulled down with a .... overall force — so it falls .... slowly.

Polly wanted to time herself in the water.

Q4 Why did people get different results? (Circle) the right words in the brackets.

It's [EASY / DIFFICULT] to measure the [TIME / SIZE] accurately, because it's difficult to [WRITE / PRESS] 'stop' on the stopwatch at [ROUGHLY / EXACTLY] the right time.

Q5 For which ball would you be most sure about the results? [Hint: if you're stuck, see Q4 on page 11.] ....

This experiment's great — I'm balled over...

If an experiment is worth doing, it's worth doing again and again. You must have got the message by now — **REPEATING RESULTS MAKES THEM MORE RELIABLE**. That's **why** you repeat them.

KS2 Science Answers — Forces in Action

Q2:

Object	Book	Worm Can	Helmet	Statue	Bag of Rats
Weight	125 g	375 g	500 g	625 g	750 g
Length of Elastic Band	15 cm	25 cm	30 cm	35 cm	40 cm

Page 14 Stretching Elastic Bands

Q1:

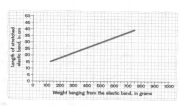

Q2: The heavier the weight hanging on the elastic band, the longer the elastic band stretches.

Q3: How much an **ELASTIC** band **STRETCHES** depends on **HOW** much **FORCE** it is being **PULLED** with.

Page 15 Stretching Elastic Bands

Q1: The "Professor Beehive" box should be ticked.

Q2: a) The binoculars weigh **250** grams. The elastic band will be **20** cm long.
b) Fido weighs **875** grams. The elastic band will be **45** cm long.
The above lengths of elastic band should be drawn onto the picture.

Page 16 Scientific Explanations

Q1: **Upthrust** is pushing up on the balloon.
Gravity is pushing down on the balloon.

Q2: Upthrust.

Q3: "The force down (weight) must be equal to the force up (upthrust)."

Q4: The **BIGGER** the balloon, the more paperclips you need to keep it at the same height.
The bigger the balloon, the **BIGGER** the upward force, so you need a **BIGGER** weight to balance out the force.

Page 17 Scientific Explanations

Q1: a)

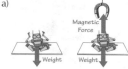

Q2: The closer the magnet is to the robot, the quicker the robot moves.
OR The further the magnet is to the robot, the less the robot moves.

Q3: "As the magnet gets closer to the robot, the magnetic force gets stronger. Once the magnetic force upwards is bigger than the weight pulling downwards, the robot moves upwards.

Page 18 Scientific Explanations

Q1:

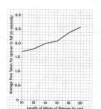

Q2: Less.

Q3: The tighter the paper is screwed up, the faster it falls into the bin. OR The less the paper is screwed up, the slower it falls.

Q4: The less surface area there is, the less air is in contact with the paper. That means that the air resistance is less so the paper ball can fall faster.
(Any answer that means the same thing is OK.)

Page 19 Mini-Project — Air Resistance

Q1: The paper spinner spins and falls to the floor. OR It spins as it falls.
(Any answer that means the same thing is OK.)

Q2: a) The missing label is "weight" or "gravity".
b) When you let go of the spinner, it **FALLS** to the ground. The forces acting on it are **AIR RESISTANCE** and weight. The **WEIGHT** is a bigger **FORCE** than the air resistance, so the spinner moves **DOWNWARDS**.

Page 20 Mini-Project — Air Resistance

Q1: "Always drop the spinner from your eye-level so it's always falling the same distance" and "Use the same spinner each time, but weigh it down with different numbers of paperclips" should be ticked.

Q2 & Q3: Should match your results, but here's the table for my spare results:

	1 paperclip	2 paperclips	3 paperclips	4 paperclips	5 paperclips	6 paperclips
1st Time (in seconds)	1.7	1.6	1.4	1.3	1.0	0.6
2nd Time (in seconds)	1.9	1.6	1.4	1.1	1.0	0.8
Average Time (in seconds)	1.8	1.6	1.4	1.2	1.0	0.7

Q4: You should make 2 measurements, to make it more accurate.

Page 21 Mini-Project — Air Resistance

Q1: Should match your results, but here's the graph for my spare results:

Q2: The more paperclips that are attached to the spinner, the faster it falls.

Q3: The spinner has weight pulling it **DOWNWARDS**, but it's being **SLOWED DOWN** by the **AIR RESISTANCE** pushing upwards. Adding more paperclips makes the spinner **HEAVIER**, but doesn't affect the air resistance. That means there's the same **UPWARDS** force from the air, but a bigger downwards force from the **WEIGHT**, so it falls **FASTER**.

Page 22 Mini-Project — Air Resistance

Q1: Possible answers are: use the same type of paper for each spinner or keep the width of the wings the same.

Q2 & Q3: Should match your results, but here's the table for my spare results:

	10 cm wings	12 cm wings	14 cm wings	16 cm wings	18 cm wings	20 cm wings
1st Time (in seconds)	1.6	1.8	1.9	2.2	2.3	2.6
2nd Time (in seconds)	1.8	1.8	2.1	2.0	2.5	2.6
Average Time (in seconds)	1.7	1.8	2.0	2.1	2.4	2.6

Page 23 Mini-Project — Air Resistance

Q1: Should match your results, but here's the graph for my spare results:

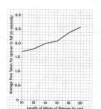

Q2: Yes — The bigger the wings, the slower the paper spinner falls.

Q3: a) The upwards force is **AIR RESISTANCE**. The downwards force is **WEIGHT** (or GRAVITY).
b) The bigger the wings, the more paper is in contact with the air, so air resistance is a bigger force and cancels out more of the weight — so it falls slower.

Page 24 Revision Questions

Q1: i) repel   ii) attract

Q2: What we call the **WEIGHT** of an object is actually just the force that attracts it **TOWARDS** the **CENTRE** of the Earth. The **HEAVIER** something is, the bigger the **FORCE** that pulls it towards the centre of the Earth.

Q3: a) The elastic band would stretch more.
b) The elastic band would stretch less.
c) The elastic band would stretch less.

Q4:

Q5: "72 ÷ 6 = 12N" should be circled.

Page 25 Revision Questions

Q6:

	Mini Bin Man	Statue	Tiny Piano
Weight in air (in Newtons)	10	20	12
Weight in water (in Newtons)	4	12	6

Q7: Gravity pulls things **TOWARDS** the ground and gives them **WEIGHT**. The **WATER** gives things an upwards push, that balances out some of the weight. The **BIGGER** an object is, the bigger the **UPWARDS** push is from the water.

Q8: The spinner has weight pulling it **DOWNWARDS**, but it's being slowed down by **AIR RESISTANCE** pushing upwards. Adding more paperclips makes the spinner **HEAVIER** but doesn't affect the air resistance. That means there's the same **UPWARDS** force from the air, but a bigger downwards force from the **WEIGHT**, so it falls **DOWNWARDS**. Keeping the weight the same and making the wings of the spinner bigger **INCREASES** the air resistance. This makes the spinner fall **SLOWER**.

BALANCING FORCES

AIR RESISTANCE

UPWARDS FORCE
Because the hot air in the balloon is lighter than normal air.

The weight and upwards forces acting on Richard's balloon are the same — so it stays the same height.

KS2 Science Answers — Forces in Action

Page 1 Background

Q1: a) Force b) The hook pulls the spring which moves the pointer.
   c) The grass.
Q2: i) attract ii) repel
Q3: a) The band will stretch more.
   b) The band will not stretch as much.
Q4: a) The air resistance is pushing up on the parachutes.
   b) The box next to the bigger parachute should be ticked.

Q5:

Page 2 Gravity

Q1:

Object	Weight (N)
Piglet	80
Mug	4
Bag	40
Bananas	9

Q2: The piglet was the heaviest.
Q3: The mug was the lightest.
Q4: What we call the **WEIGHT** of an object is the force that attracts it **TOWARDS** the Earth. The **HEAVIER** something is, the bigger the **FORCE** that pulls it towards the Earth.

Page 3 Gravity

Q1: i) The answer "b) 12 ÷ 6 = 2N" should be circled.
   ii) 6 ÷ 6 = 1 cm
   iii) Wilma would be able to hit a golf ball further on the Moon.
Q2: Walking on the Moon would feel quite wobbly, and you would fall to the ground slower between steps. (Any reasonable answer is OK.)

Page 4 Gravity

Q1: The yo-yo is being pulled towards the centre of the Earth, which is straight down. (Any reasonable answer is OK.)

Q2:

Q3: a) The rain always falls towards the centre of the Earth.
   b)

Q4: Laura, Ed and Malcolm don't fall off the Earth because gravity pulls them towards the centre of the Earth, even in Australia.

Page 5 Multiple Forces

Q1: a) Upwards push of air from hairdryer.
     Weight of teddy bear (or gravity).
   b) Pull up from spring.
     Weight of monkey (or gravity).
   c) Pull from magnet.
     Weight of car (or gravity).
   d) Pull up from spring.
     Weight of 10 kg mass.
   e) Pull from string.
     Weight of 10 kg mass (or gravity).

Page 6 Multiple Forces

Q1:

Q2: The boxes next to the cannon and the jack-in-the-box should be ticked.

Page 7 Multiple Forces

Q1:

(For all of them, "Gravity" is OK instead of "Weight".)

Page 8 Forces in Water

Q1:

	Black Ball	Binoculars	Spiky Club	White Ball
Weight in air (in Newtons)	8	10	20	16
Weight in water (in Newtons)	2	6	14	10

Q2: The objects weighed less in water than they did in air.
Q3: When an object is under the **WATER**, the water gives it an **UPWARD** push that **CANCELS OUT** some of the object's **WEIGHT**.

Page 9 Forces in Water

Q1:

Size of Hollow Ball	Forcemeter Reading in Air (Newtons)	Forcemeter Reading in Water (Newtons)	Upward Push from the Water (Newtons)
Small	3.0	2.5	0.5
Medium	3.0	2.0	1.0
Large	3.0	1.5	1.5
Extra Large	3.0	1.0	2.0

Q2:

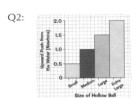

Q3: **GRAVITY** pulls things towards the ground and gives them weight. The water gives things an **UPWARD** push, that **BALANCES OUT** some of the weight. The bigger an object is, the **BIGGER** the **UPWARD** push is from the water.

Page 10 Forces in Water

Q1: All of the things in the picture have gravity and the upward push from the water acting on them — apart from the shark and walrus in the hammock who are not touching the water. (The two crabs on the sea bed also have an upward push from the ground.)

Page 11 Doing Things More Than Once

Q1:

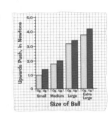

Q2: a) No.
   b) Ugmina always got higher results than Ogbert.
Q3: Sometimes it's **DIFFICULT** to read the forcemeter accurately because the **POINTER** can wobble up and down a bit.
Q4: The "Medium" box should be ticked.

Page 12 Doing Things More Than Once

Q1:

Size of Hollow Ball	Small	Medium	Large	Extra Large
Bob's Results	0.9 secs	1.4 secs	1.7 secs	2.0 secs
Liz's Results	1.2 secs	1.5 secs	1.7 secs	2.0 secs
Ed's Results	1.2 secs	1.4 secs	1.6 secs	2.0 secs
Sue's Results	1.1 secs	1.3 secs	1.5 secs	1.9 secs
Nav's Results	1.1 secs	1.5 secs	1.7 secs	2.0 secs

Q2: "The bigger the ball is, the slower it falls" should be ticked.
Q3: The **BIGGER** the ball, the more it's slowed down by the water resistance and the air trapped inside. All the balls weighed the **SAME**, so they were all pulled down by gravity the **SAME**. But the bigger the ball, the **BIGGER** the upward push it gets from the water, so it's pulled down with a **SMALLER** overall force — so it falls **MORE** slowly.
Q4: It's **DIFFICULT** so measure the **TIME** accurately, because it's difficult to **PRESS** 'stop' on the stopwatch at **EXACTLY** the right time.
Q5: Extra Large.

Page 13 Stretching Elastic Bands

Q1: "Only change the object hanging from each elastic band each time and nothing else", "Do the whole experiment on Earth — don't weigh some objects on Earth, and some objects on the Moon where things weigh less" and "Make sure that the elastic bands that were used were all the same size and shape" should all be ticked.

Stretching Elastic Bands

The other day I was fiddling with elastic bands and I noticed that when you hang something on one, it gets longer. To find out more about <u>how long</u> an elastic band gets when you hang <u>different weights</u> from it, I did an experiment. Here's a photo* of it:

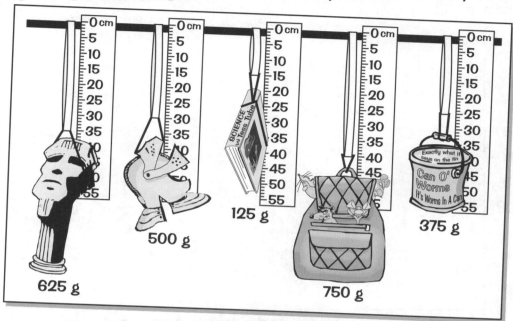

125 g

500 g

375 g

625 g

750 g

*If that's a photo, I'm a monkey's uncle.

Q1   It was important to make this a <u>fair test</u>. Tick ✔ the three things that would make the elastic band experiment a fair test.

☐ Make sure all the objects weighed exactly the same.

☐ Make sure all the objects were the same size and shape.

☐ Only change the object hanging from each elastic band each time and nothing else.

☐ Make sure that the elastic bands that were used were all the same size and shape.

☐ Do the whole experiment on Earth — don't weigh some objects on Earth, and some objects on the Moon where things weigh less.

☐ Hold onto the object to pull it down as far as the elastic band will go.

Q2   Fill in this table of how long the elastic bands were with different weights hanging off them. Use the picture to tell you the weights and how long the bands were.

Object	Book	Worm Can	Helmet	Statue	Bag of Rats
Weight					
Length of Elastic Band					

No stretching in here — elastic's banned...

You can try this stuff for yourself — just hang something from an elastic band and see the band get longer. The <u>heavier</u> the object is, the <u>further</u> the elastic band will stretch — makes sense really.

Stretching Elastic Bands

On page 13 you completed a table of the results of the elastic band experiment,
but it'll be <u>easier</u> to see what's <u>going on</u> if you turn it into a <u>graph</u>.

Q1   Draw a line graph for the results in the table on page 13.   For help on drawing line graphs, look at
page 93 of the Maths Study Guide.

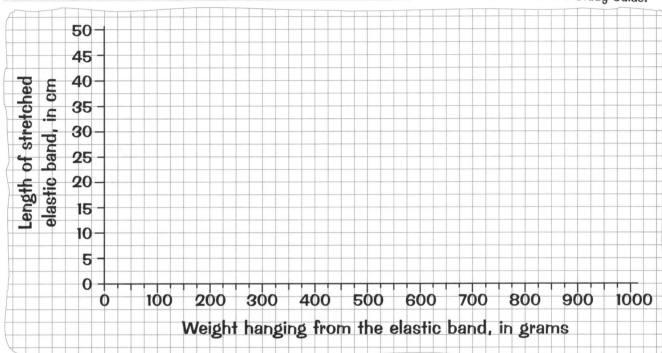

Length of stretched elastic band, in cm

Weight hanging from the elastic band, in grams

Q2   Look at the graph. Finish off
this <u>description</u> of the results.

The heavier the weight hanging on the elastic band,

....

....

If people do experiments with elastic bands,
do elastic bands do experiments with people?

Q3   Choose from the words on the weight to finish
this <u>explanation</u> of <u>why</u> the results are like that.

How much an .... band ....

depends on .... much .... it

is being .... with.

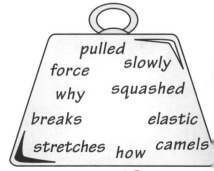

pulled
force   slowly
why   squashed
breaks   elastic
stretches   how   camels

Weight a minute — I'm just hanging around...

Results in a table are all well and good, but sometimes a <u>graph</u> is just the thing for finding out what
an experiment has told you. It makes it so much easier to see what's going on — useful stuff.

Stretching Elastic Bands

Once you've done the graph for the elastic band experiment on page 14, you can use it to work out <u>how long</u> the elastic band will be if you hang <u>different</u> weights from it.

Q1 Dr. X says if one of the elastic bands has a nasty bear hanging off it, it'll stretch to 45 cm. Professor Beehive says that it'll be 50 cm long. The bear weighs 1000 g. Who is right?

[Hint: use a ruler to continue the line on the graph on page 14 up to 1000 g, then read off the length.]

 Dr. X    Professor Beehive

Q2 How long would the elastic band be with these objects hanging on it? Read the weights from the scales, and use the graph on page 14 to work out how long the elastic band would be. Then draw the stretched elastic band in the box — use the ruler to get it the right size.

a)

The binoculars weigh .... grams.

The elastic band will be .... cm long.

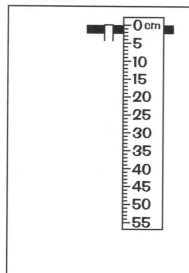

```
┌ 0 cm
├ 5
├ 10
├ 15
├ 20
├ 25
├ 30
├ 35
├ 40
├ 45
├ 50
└ 55
```

b)

Fido weighs .... grams.

The elastic band will be .... cm long.

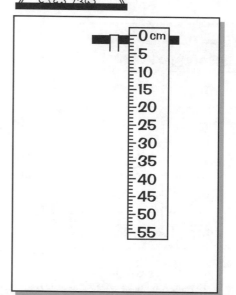

```
┌ 0 cm
├ 5
├ 10
├ 15
├ 20
├ 25
├ 30
├ 35
├ 40
├ 45
├ 50
└ 55
```

Use a ruler to measure — how about the Queen...

It's tons easier to predict results by using a <u>graph</u> than straight from a <u>table</u>. Predicting how much a dog would stretch the elastic band just by using the table would be <u>pretty darn tough</u>.

Scientific Explanations

Sometimes when you do an experiment it's okay to explain what's happening in <u>everyday language</u> — but sometimes you've got to use impressive <u>scientific</u> words to make things <u>totally clear</u>.

Q1 I've just let go of this helium-filled balloon.
The arrows show the directions of the forces on it.
Name the forces using the words in the bubble.

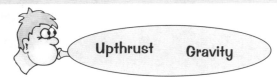

.... is pushing up on the balloon.

.... is pulling down on the balloon.

Q2 When I let go of the balloon, it rises to the ceiling.
Which of the two forces from Q1 must be bigger?

....

Q3 Katie is attaching paperclips to 5 different-sized helium balloons to weigh them down and keep all the balloons at the same height.
To keep the balloon at the same height, the forces must be balanced.
Put a tick ✔ by the sentence that describes a balloon with balanced forces.

The force up (upthrust) must be bigger than the force down (weight). ☐

The force down (weight) must be bigger than the force up (upthrust). ☐

The force down (weight) must be equal to the force up (upthrust). ☐

 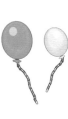

Q4 This table shows how many paperclips Katie needed to keep each balloon at the same height.

size of balloon	number of paperclips
small	9
big	14
medium	11
huge	18
tiny	8

These are the balloons from Q3.

Use the results to find a pattern — then finish this sentence using either BIGGER or SMALLER.

The .... the balloon, the more paperclips you need to keep it at the same height.

Now you need to give a scientific explanation for what's going on. Fill in the gaps using words from the brackets.

The bigger the balloon, the .... (BIGGER / SMALLER) the upward force, so you need a ....

(BIGGER / SMALLER) weight to balance out the force.

Sheep jousting — baa-lance...

To keep a helium balloon at the same height, you have to <u>balance</u> the forces on it. A <u>bigger</u> balloon will need <u>more</u> paperclips to stop it floating upwards. Or you could just tie it to a chair...

Scientific Explanations

Same sort of thing on this page, but thinking about <u>magnets</u> instead of balloons.

1 a) My robot, CGP-0, is sitting on a table. Draw and label an arrow to show the direction of the WEIGHT force acting on him.

b) Now there's a magnet above CGP-0. Write on the forces WEIGHT and MAGNETIC FORCE that act on him, with arrows to show the directions.

2 I've done an experiment where I changed the height of the magnet above CGP-0 to see if he moved or not. Look for a pattern, and then write how the distance of the magnet above the robot affects how he moves.

Distance of magnet above CGP-0	20 cm	15 cm	10 cm	5 cm
Did CGP-0 move?	Not at all.	He wobbles a bit but doesn't leave the table.	He wobbles, then jumps up and sticks to the magnet.	He jumps up and sticks to the magnet.

....

....

....

3 Think about a good scientific explanation for this pattern. Tick ✔ the box next to the correct explanation.

Magnets never work when they're further than 10 cm away. That's why the robot didn't move. ☐

The magnet was broken. ☐

All those magnets were playing havoc with CGP-0's electronics.

When the magnet's more than 20 cm away, the robot doesn't feel any magnetic force. When it gets closer, it suddenly feels the force and moves. ☐

The robot was scared of magnets. ☐

As the magnet gets closer to the robot, the magnetic force gets stronger. Once the magnetic force upwards is bigger than the weight pulling downwards, the robot moves upwards. ☐

The nearer the magnet gets, the lighter the robot gets, so the easier it moves. ☐

I love magnets — they're really attractive...

You can get strong magnets and weak magnets, but all of them pull <u>harder</u> if you're <u>close</u> to things. Otherwise your paperclips would be pulled by big magnets miles away — that'd be weird.

Scientific Explanations

That's enough about balloons and magnets — now you can
think about what happens when something <u>falls</u> through the <u>air</u>.

Q1 This screwed up ball of paper is falling
through the air. Draw on the two
forces acting on it and label them.

Q2  Vincent is a struggling artist. He's trying to paint a portrait of his pet
turtle, Tim. After his first mistake, he drops the page in the bin.
The next time, he folds the paper before dropping it.
After that, he screws it up. The angrier Vincent gets, the
tighter he screws up the paper before dropping it in the bin.

Tim gets bored of sitting still, so he starts timing how long
each piece of paper takes to fall. Here are his results.

State of paper	flat piece of paper	folded in half	lightly screwed up ball	tightly screwed up ball	very tight ball
Time taken to drop	20 seconds	17 seconds	10 seconds	6 seconds	4 seconds

The amount of paper that is in contact with the air is called the surface area.
Does screwing up the paper make the surface area more or less? ....

Q3 Write down any pattern that you can see in the times taken to drop into the bin.

....

....

Q4 Write a scientific explanation for this pattern — think about the surface
area of the paper and the forces acting on the paper as it falls. (If you're
stuck, look back at the last 2 pages for good examples of scientific explanations.)

....

....

....

Little did Vincent know
that Tim was doing some
painting of his own.

Don't screw up your scientific explanations...

If you screw a piece of paper up, it falls <u>faster</u> — there's <u>less surface area</u> for the air to touch.
That's why paper aeroplanes never look like screwed-up balls — they'd fall to the ground <u>too fast</u>.

Mini-Project — Air Resistance

MINI-PROJECT

This mini-project is about <u>paper spinners</u> — and what makes them fall faster.

Discover the Art of Paper Spinner Making

① Start by cutting out two rectangles of paper, 10 cm long and 2 cm wide.

↔ 10 cm ↔ 2 cm

② Put the two pieces together.

Then fold the two ends over, 2 cm from the edge.

↔ 2 cm

③ Stick a ⇒ paperclip on the end to hold them together.

④ Fold one side upwards.

⑤ And fold the other side downwards.

⑥ Ta daa. A paper spinner. Smashing.

1 Hold the paper spinner with the paperclip end at the bottom. Hold it level with your eye, then drop it and watch how it moves.

Describe the movement of the paper spinner as it falls to the floor.

....

....

2
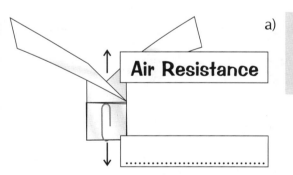
Air Resistance

a) There are two forces on the spinner when you let go of it. I've put labels on them, but I've left one blank for you to fill in.

....

> The upward force on Jon's parachute was more than just air resistance.

b) Finish these sentences about how the forces on the spinner make it move when you drop it.

When you let go of the spinner, it .... to the ground. The forces on it

are .... and weight. The .... is a bigger

.... than the air resistance, so the spinner moves ....

All this action — it's got me in a right spin...

OK, so weight pulls things <u>downwards</u>, and air tries to push them <u>upwards</u>. Things fall to the floor when there's nothing holding them up because the weight is a <u>bigger force</u> than the air resistance.

MINI-PROJECT

Mini-Project — Air Resistance

This page is about finding out whether the <u>weight</u> of the paper spinner makes a difference to how quickly it falls.

For this experiment, you'll need:
a paper spinner...
... 6 paperclips...
... and a stopwatch.

How to do the experiment:
1) Weigh down the paper spinner with some paperclips.
2) Drop the spinner from eye-level and time how long it takes to fall to the floor.
3) Change the number of paperclips and do it again.

Q1 Pick two things that would help make your experiment sensible and make it a fair test. Tick ✔ the right answers.

Always drop the spinner from your eye-level so it's always falling the same distance.

Put a parachute on the heavier spinners.

Use the same spinner and the same number of paperclips so it's the same shape, size and weight each time.

Use the same spinner each time, but weigh it down with different numbers of paperclips.

Holly attached loads of paperclips to her spinner...

Q2 Do the experiment. Start with just one paperclip on the spinner. Time how long it takes to fall from eye-level and write the result in the table, then do it again. Then repeat the whole thing for 2, 3, 4, 5, 6 paperclips. (If you can't do the experiment, use my spare results at the bottom).

	1 paperclip	2 paperclips	3 paperclips	4 paperclips	5 paperclips	6 paperclips
1st Time (in seconds)						
2nd Time (in seconds)						
Average Time (in seconds)						

Q3 Work out the average of each pair of results, and write it in the 'average' row of the table.

To work out the average, add the two results together and divide by 2.

Q4 Why do you think it's important to take two measurements for each weight of spinner?

....

Spare Results: 1 paperclip 1.7s/1.9s, 2 paperclips 1.6s/1.6s, 3 paperclips 1.4s/1.4s, 4 paperclips 1.3s/1.1s, 5 paperclips 1s/1s, 6 paperclips 0.6s/0.8s.

Paper... scissors... stone... paper... scissors... paperclips?

The spinners fall pretty fast, so you've got to be ultra-careful with that stopwatch. Make sure you watch really carefully and press the button <u>exactly</u> when you drop it and <u>exactly</u> when it lands.

Mini-Project — Air Resistance

It's <u>no good</u> just doing experiments <u>all</u> the time
— you've got to be able to look at results and work out <u>what's going on</u>.
Otherwise there's no point in doing them.

Q1 Look at the results table on the last page.

Use the row of average times to draw a line graph on this piece of graph paper.

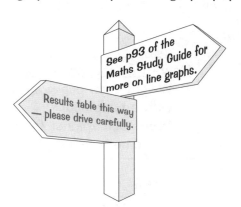

See p93 of the Maths Study Guide for more on line graphs.

Results table this way — please drive carefully.

Q2 Look at the graph you've drawn. How does the number of paperclips affect how quickly the spinner falls?

....

....

....

....

Graph: Average Time Taken for spinner to fall (in seconds) [y-axis: 0, 0.5, 1.0, 1.5, 2.0] vs Number of Paperclips Attached to Spinner [x-axis: 1, 2, 3, 4, 5, 6]

Heavier objects don't always fall faster. If there's no air, like on the Moon, a feather falls as fast as a brick. In this experiment, the heavier spinners only fall quicker because the air resistance doesn't make as much difference to them.

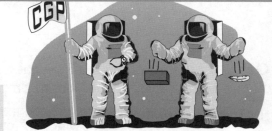

Q3 Here's a scientific conclusion about what's happening. (Circle) the right words from the brackets to make it right.

The spinner has weight pulling it [downwards / upwards], but it's

being [speeded up / slowed down] by the [air resistance / air speed] pushing upwards.

Adding more paperclips makes the spinner [bigger / heavier], but doesn't affect the air

resistance. That means there's the same [downwards / upwards] force from the air,

but a bigger downwards force from the [weight / wind], so it falls [faster / slower].

Do what they say — resistance is useless...

Air resistance is the <u>same</u> for objects the <u>same</u> size — but when they have different <u>weights</u> the heavier object will have more weight-force acting against the air resistance and will fall faster.

MINI-PROJECT

Mini-Project — Air Resistance

I bet weight's not the only thing that affects how fast a spinner falls — there coul
be loads of things: the <u>height</u> you drop it from, the <u>length</u> of wings, the <u>thickness</u> of paper..

This experiment is to find out if <u>different lengths of wings</u> change how quickly a spinner falls.

You're going to need:

6 paper spinners, the same width, made of the
same paper, with different length wings: 10 cm,
12 cm, 14 cm, 16 cm, 18 cm and 20 cm...   ... and the old trusty stopwatch.

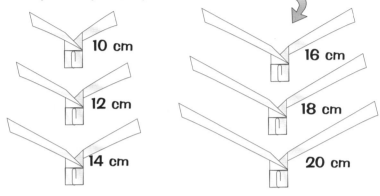

10 cm

12 cm

14 cm

16 cm

18 cm

20 cm

<u>How to do the experiment:</u>
1) Weight each paper spinner down
   with a paperclip.
2) Drop each spinner from eye-level
   and time how long it takes to fall.

Q1 I've thought of two ways you can make your
experiment a fair test, but I'm sure there are more.
Write down one more way in the space I've left.

1)   Keep the spinners the same weight
     (by using the same number of paperclips).

2)   Drop the spinners from the same height each time.

3)   ....

     ....

Bob thought he had to drop
a different kind of spinner...

Q2 Do the experiment. Time each spinner twice and write the results
in this table. Remember to drop them all from the same height.

*If you can't do the experiment,
you could make up the results.
er... I mean, you could use the
Spare Results at the bottom.*

	10 cm wings	12 cm wings	14 cm wings	16 cm wings	18 cm wings	20 cm wings
1st Time (in seconds)						
2nd Time (in seconds)						
Average Time (in seconds)						

Q3 Work out the average of each pair of results, and write it in the 'Average Time' row.

Aaaargh — I hate spiders...

When you know what you want to test (how fast spinners fall) the best plan is to work out what all
the different things that might affect it are (length of wings, weight...), and test them all <u>separately</u>.

Mini-Project — Air Resistance

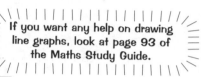

It's the moment of truth. Does the length of the wings really change how quickly a paper spinner falls to the ground...

I guess you'd better draw a graph and find out.

Q1 Use the average times from page 22 to draw a line graph on this paper here:

If you want any help on drawing line graphs, look at page 93 of the Maths Study Guide.

Average Time Taken for spinner to fall (in seconds)

3.0
2.5
2.0
1.5
1.0
0.5
0

Length of Wings of Spinner (in cm)
10   12   14   16   18   20

Look at the graph you've drawn.

Q2 Does the length of wings affect how quickly the spinner falls? If so, what effect does it have?

YES ☐   NO ☐

....

....

....

Jen wanted to know if different length wings made a difference to how quickly ducks fall.

Q3 There are two forces on a paper spinner when it's falling through the air (see page 19).

a) What are these two forces?

The upwards force is ....

The downwards force is ....

To give a good scientific explanation, you need to say what the results are and use the science facts you know to explain why they happened.

b) Give a good scientific explanation of why you got the results you did in this experiment.

....

....

It's coming at you — duck...

Don't go thinking this isn't <u>real</u> science. This is <u>exactly</u> the kind of thing scientists have to do when they <u>design</u> a new aeroplane. Ok, they do it with metal, not paper, but it's the same kind of thing.

Revision Questions

There's a <u>lot</u> of questions down there, but don't go into some sort of arm-flapping panic — all these questions are really similar to ones in the rest of the book. Remember 2 things: <u>breathe</u> and <u>answer</u>

Q1   Write next to each pair of magnets what they'll do to each other — 'attract' or 'repel'.

 ....

 ....

Q2   Choose the right words from those in the cloud to make the sentences about force correct.

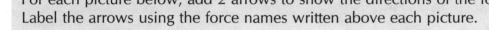

weight   speed   edge   force   centre   heavier   lighter   size   towards   away from

What we call the .... of an object is actually just the force that attracts it

.... the .... of the Earth. The .... something is,

the bigger the .... that pulls it towards the centre of the Earth.

Q3   Here's a dumb-bell hanging on an elastic band. What will happen to the band if...

a) I hang a heavier dumb-bell on it? ....

b) I hang a lighter dumb-bell on it? ....

c) I hang the same dumb-bell in water? ....

Q4   For each picture below, add 2 arrows to show the directions of the forces.
Label the arrows using the force names written above each picture.

a) Add these forces: 'kick' and 'gravity'.

b) Add these forces: 'gravity' and 'upward push of water'.

c) Add these forces: 'gravity' and 'upthrust'.

Q5   Paul weighs 72 Newtons on Earth. How much would he weigh on the Moon? (Circle) the right answer — remember gravity is six times stronger on the Earth than it is on the Moon.

a) 72 ÷ 2 = 36N   b) 72 ÷ 6 = 12N   c) 72 ÷ 6 = 24N   d) 72 × 6 = 432N

Gravity vs. Upthrust — Tonight's Big Match Live...

It's probably not what you want to hear, but I'm gonna say it anyway — <u>check</u> all of your answers at <u>least</u> once to make sure you've done it right. That way you can be sure not to make any silly <u>imstakes</u>.

Revision Questions

If you're still <u>breathing</u> and still <u>answering</u> — good, only three more questions to go
and then you can sit back and rest with a sparkling lemonade on the beach.

6   Look at the forcemeters and fill in this table of the weights for objects in air and in water.

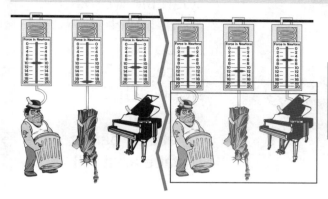

	Mini Bin Man	Statue	Tiny Piano
Weight in air (in Newtons)			
Weight in water (in Newtons)			

7   (Circle) the right words in the brackets to finish this conclusion about the results above.

Gravity pulls things [TOWARDS / AWAY FROM] the ground and gives them [TROUBLE / WEIGHT].

The [WATER / GRAVITY] gives things an upwards push, that balances out some of the weight.

The [BIGGER / SMALLER] an object is, the bigger the [UPWARD / SIDEWAYS] push is from the water.

8   Here's a scientific conclusion about what's happening to a spinner when you make it
bigger or add more paperclips to it. Fill in the blanks with words from the giant paperclip.

The spinner has weight pulling it ...., but it's

being slowed down by .... pushing upwards.

Adding more paperclips makes the spinner .... ,

but doesn't affect the air resistance. That means there's the same

.... force from the air, but a bigger downwards

force from the .... , so it falls

.... Keeping the weight the same and making the

wings of the spinner bigger .... the air resistance.

This makes the spinner fall ....

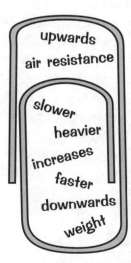

upwards
air resistance
slower
heavier
increases
faster
downwards
weight

Hair that won't do what you want? — No, that's HAIR resistance...

Once upon a time, in a land far away, lived a man with a big thumb and a cat with an eye patch and they lived
happily ever after because they'd read "Year 6 — Forces in Action". Hmm, maybe I <u>won't</u> write story books.

Index